In ancient times, the Roman ruler ordered a count to be taken of all the people who lived in the Roman Empire. Each person went to the town where he was born to be counted.

A man named Joseph left his home
in Nazareth and traveled to Bethlehem.
His wife, Mary, who was expecting her
first baby, went with him.

While they were in Bethlehem,
Mary gave birth to a baby boy.
They were staying in a stable
because there were no rooms
left for them to rent.

Mary wrapped
the baby in a soft
blanket and placed
him on the straw
in the manger.

Outside the city, shepherds were sleeping in the fields so they could protect their flocks of sheep. God sent an angel to tell the shepherds the great news, but the angel was shining so brightly that the shepherds were afraid.

The angel spoke to the shepherds and told them he was bringing them wonderful news that was for all the people on earth.

"Today in the town of David, a Savior has been born to you; he is Christ the Lord. This will be a sign to you: You will find the baby wrapped in cloth and lying in a manger."

Suddenly more angels appeared and they were all praising God and saying, "Glory to God in the highest, and on earth peace, good will toward men."

After the angels returned to heaven, the shepherds hurried to Bethlehem to see this newborn baby.

"Let us go to Bethlehem to see this thing that has happened, which the Lord has told us about," they said to one another.

There they found Mary, and Joseph,
and the baby, who was lying in
a manger, just as the angel
had told them.

The shepherds were
so amazed by all
this that they
told everyone
they saw about
the blessed
new baby.

Mary was happy.
She kept these memories
and treasured them
in her heart.